Marco

He's a joke...
messing a...
always me...
if he some...
things wrong.

Waxy Max

He's very sporty and
football mad. On the
outside, he's tough,
but underneath he's
got the biggest heart.

Philippa Feltpen

A real peacemaker, she
helps keep the other
Pens in order by sorting
out arguments and giving
good advice.

Splodge,
do you like
cake?

Squiggle and Splodge

The Scribble twins! They're
both quiet, both shy. Although
they may not look alike, they
do almost everything together.

Enter ...

Splodge, I'm so excited!

Me too!!

Pens

Helping you to get to know God more

Excited!

Written by
Alexa Tewkesbury

Every day a short Bible reading is brought to life with the help of the Pens characters. A related question and prayer apply this to daily life. Written in four sections, two focusing on the lives of Pens and two on Bible characters, young children will be inspired to learn more of God and His Word.

What's inside?

God's Good Plans — Day 1

On God's Side – Chosen — Day 10

Super — Day 16

Once Upon a Mountain Top – Jesus shines! — Day 25

CWR

FSC
www.fsc.org

MIX
Paper from
responsible sources
FSC® C015900

GOD'S GOOD PLANS

'The LORD says, "I will teach you the way you should go"' (Psalm 32 v 8)

The Perfect Cake

Sharpy was waiting for Max in the kitchen.

Are you ready, Sharpy?

We're going to make the *best* cake ever.

SUGAR

Max put all the ingredients on the table. He needed flour, sugar, eggs and butter.

When Denzil and Charlotte knocked on the door, Max said, 'We're making a cake. Would you like to help?'

'Of course we would!' grinned Denzil. 'I love cake.'

'I always think living how God wants us to is a bit like making a cake,' said Charlotte. 'If we follow His recipe and obey Him, the cake we make will be perfect!'

In the Bible, God gives us the perfect recipe for how to live our lives.

FLOUR

What is your favourite sort of cake?

Pens Prayer
Father God, please help me to listen to You and obey You. Amen.

God's Good Plans

'love the LORD your God'
(Joshua 22 v 5)

Lots of love

Max spilt some sugar on the kitchen floor. Quick as a flash, Sharpy licked it up.

'Sharpy loves sweet things, doesn't he?' laughed Denzil.

'Too much!' grinned Max.

'And "love",' added Charlotte, 'is the most important ingredient in God's recipe for living our lives in the best way.'

'Not love for sugar, though,' giggled Denzil.

'No!' smiled Charlotte. 'God wants us to love *Him*. Not just a tiny bit. Not even a medium-sized bit. God wants us to love Him with our WHOLE HEARTS. That means making Him the most important Person in our lives.'

 When we obey God, we show Him how much we love Him.

What other ways can you think of to show God that you love Him?

Pens Prayer

Thank You, dear God, for all the ways You show me You love me. Please teach me to love You, too. Amen.

Day 3 God's Good Plans

'do his will' (Joshua 22 v 5)

God's Will

Denzil stirred up the ingredients in Max's cake. Max dipped in a teaspoon and tasted a little scoop of the mixture.

'The next step in God's recipe,' said Charlotte, 'is to mix love up with lots of doing what God wants us to do.'

'Like what?' Denzil asked.

'Like being kind to each other,' answered Charlotte. 'Helping each other. Sharing what we have. *And* saying sorry to God for the wrong things we sometimes do. God knows we find it hard not to make mistakes. But He always forgives us when we ask Him to.'

God only has good plans for us. So let's do as He asks us to.

This week, how could you be kind? What could you do to help? What could you share?

Pens Prayer

Teach me, God, to live Your way every day. Amen.

9

God's Good Plans

'obey his commandments'
(Joshua 22 v 5)

Special rules

Vicki Quill's Special Cake Bakery

I think this cake's ready to bake.

I'll just read my recipe to check that I haven't forgotten anything.

'We can check what's in God's recipe, too,' smiled Charlotte. 'His instructions are all in the Bible. Some are called God's "commandments". They're His special rules.'

'What special rules?' asked Max.

'They tell us to do things like put God first and obey our parents,' answered Charlotte. 'And they tell us NOT to do things like hurting each other, telling lies, stealing or being jealous of anyone. Obeying God's rules helps us to live God's way.'

 God's rules are there to help us make the most of every day.

What rules does your school have?

Pens Prayer

Thank You, Father God, that You have made rules because You love me and want to keep me safe. Amen.

Day 5 — God's Good Plans

'be faithful to him' (Joshua 22 v 5)

Faithful

Max took a big, round baking tin out of his cupboard. Denzil helped him to pour the cake mixture into it.

Sharpy licked his lips.

Won't be long now, Sharpy.

'Sharpy's such a faithful friend,' smiled Charlotte. 'Being faithful is another ingredient in God's perfect cake mix. God wants us to be faithful to *Him*.'

'So let's copy Sharpy,' grinned Max. 'He sticks with me whatever happens. He never forgets that I take care of him, and he just loves being around me.'

'Cool,' nodded Denzil. 'Which is just what a faithful friend should do.'

 God sticks with us. Let's stick with Him, too.

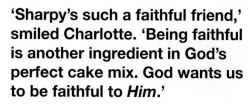

Who are your faithful friends? Say their names and thank God for them now.

Pens Prayer

Dear Father, there is so much to see and to do every day. But please help me never to forget You. Amen.

Day 6 — God's Good Plans

'serve him with all your heart and soul'
(Joshua 22 v 5)

Excited!

Max's oven was hot and ready to bake the cake.

Carefully, he opened the oven door and pushed the tin inside.

'This really is going to be the best cake ever!' Max beamed.

'I hope so,' answered Denzil. 'We've worked *very* hard to make it.'

'God loves to see us working hard at things,' said Charlotte. 'There's a big dollop of excitement in His recipe for living our lives in the best way. He wants us to be happy in everything we do. Most of all, He wants us to be wholehearted about following Him.'

 Let's not be half-hearted towards God. It's time to get excited about Him!

What's the difference between being 'wholehearted' and being 'half-hearted'?

Pens Prayer

Lord God, You are amazing! Praise You! Amen.

God's Good Plans

'love your neighbors as you love yourself.' (Leviticus 19 v 18)

Sharing and caring

There was still a little bit of cake mixture in the mixing bowl.

Who'd like some cake mix?

We can scrape out the bowl while we're waiting for the cake to bake.

Denzil looked doubtful.

'There's not much there,' he said. 'You'd better eat it up yourself.'

'No!' replied Max. 'You're my friends and I want to share it with you.'

'That's something else you'll find in God's recipe,' Charlotte smiled. 'Caring for other people. God wants us to look after each other in the same way as we look after ourselves.'

God's plan isn't for us to be selfish. He wants us to be kind and to love each other.

If one of your friends is selfish about something, how does it make you feel?

Pens Prayer

Father God, it's easy to think about what I want. Please help me to see what other people may want or need, too. Amen.

Day 8 — **God's Good Plans**

'God is always at work in you'
(Philippians 2 v 13)

Just right

As the cake cooked, the kitchen filled with the scrumptious smell of baking.

Cake mixture is yummy.

But when it's been baked, it tastes even better.

'It's the heat from the oven that turns the mixture into a cake,' Max nodded.

Charlotte chuckled. 'The oven makes the ingredients work!' she grinned. 'And God makes *His* recipe work, too. He doesn't leave us on our own to try to live His way. He stays close to help us get the mix just right. He wants us to make the most of our lives by obeying His instructions.'

 When we ask Him to help, God will be at work in us every day.

Is there anything in God's recipe that you'd like Him to help you with? Why not ask Him now?

Pens Prayer

Dear God, You know that following Your recipe isn't always easy. Thank You for helping me. Amen.

Day 9 God's Good Plans

'Find out for yourself how good the LORD is.' (Psalm 34 v 8)

The tastiest way

At last the cake was ready. Max took it carefully out of the oven to cool.

'How long before we can try it?' asked Denzil.

'Soon,' smiled Max.

And soon indeed, Denzil, Max and Charlotte were munching a slice of cake. Max gave a small piece to Sharpy, too.

'Mmm, perfect!' beamed Max.

'Perfectly perfect!' nodded Denzil.

'Gorgeous,' agreed Charlotte. 'God's recipe for our lives is perfect as well,' she added. 'All we have to do is learn to follow His plans to live in the best way we can. God's way is definitely the tastiest way!'

Let's try God's recipe and see how good it is.

Can you remember the ingredients in God's recipe?

Pens Prayer
Thank You, Lord God, for teaching me to follow YOUR GREAT PLAN for my life. Amen.

21

Day 10

'I chose you before I gave you life'
(Jeremiah 1 v 5)

God's words

Jeremiah was a man who loved God.

Even before Jeremiah was born, God had chosen him to do a very important job.

'There are things I need you to tell my people,' God said.

Jeremiah felt worried. 'Why me?' he asked. 'I'm too young to do something important like that. What will I say?'

'Don't be afraid,' God said. 'I'll take care of you.'

God reached out a hand and touched Jeremiah's lips.

'Here you are,' God smiled. 'I am giving you the words I want you to say.'

Jeremiah was afraid, but he knew God's plans were good.

If you feel worried, do you tell God like Jeremiah did? God will always help you.

Pens Prayer

Dear Lord, thank You that I am special to You. Amen.

On God's Side
Chosen

Day 11

About time

Jeremiah listened to God. He heard the words God wanted him to say to His people, the Israelites.

And Jeremiah knew that God was sad.

God had been kind to the Israelites. He had helped them and looked after them. He had never left them.

But they had stopped listening to Him. They wouldn't do as He asked them to. Or live the way He wanted them to.

Now God needed Jeremiah to tell them to turn back to Him.

It was time for them to put things right and be His friends again.

Jeremiah loved God and knew that he must obey Him.

How has God been kind to you?

Pens Prayer

Thank You, Father God, for all the ways You are kind to me. Please teach me to listen to You. Amen.

'They will not defeat you, for I will be with you to protect you.' (Jeremiah 1 v 19)

Whatever happens

'Are you ready, Jeremiah?' God asked.

'Yes, Lord,' Jeremiah answered.

'What I'm asking you to do won't be easy,' God said. 'No one will like the things you say. They won't want to listen to you because they don't want to listen to *me*. Everyone will turn against you. But,' God added, 'you will have me on your side. Whatever happens, I will look after you.'

When we obey God, He is always on our side.

How do you think Jeremiah felt when God said that people would turn against him?

Pens Prayer

Lord God, as I grow bigger, please help me to be like Jeremiah – ready to stand up for You. Amen.

On God's Side

Chosen

Day 13

'Let's bring charges against [Jeremiah] and stop listening to what he says.'
(Jeremiah 18 v 18)

Jeremiah keeps talking

God was right.

The more Jeremiah spoke to God's special people, the more they didn't like what he had to say.

Some of them even complained to the king.

'Jeremiah doesn't want to help us!' they cried. 'All he wants to do is hurt us. He should be locked up!'

But Jeremiah didn't stop talking to them.

He didn't stop speaking the words God wanted them to hear.

God had given Jeremiah a job to do and he was going to do it.

God's people didn't want to obey God. They wanted to carry on living selfishly.

What does 'being selfish' mean? How can you be 'unselfish'?

Pens Prayer

Father, please teach me to be unselfish. I want to live the way You want me to. Every day. Amen.

'do what you want to with him; I can't stop you.' (Jeremiah 38 v 5)

Into the Well

The king didn't know what to do.

Jeremiah was telling him to obey God.

But the people were moaning to him about Jeremiah. They wanted to get rid of him.

At last the king said, 'Oh, go on then. There's nothing I can do to stop you, is there? Go and do what you want.'

So the people fetched Jeremiah.

They led him to an empty well.

And they dropped him deep down inside.

With God beside him, Jeremiah was far braver than the king.

What do you usually find inside a well?

Pens Prayer

Lord, if bad things happen, thank You that You are always with me. Amen.

On God's Side
Chosen

Day 15

'what these men have done is wrong.'
(Jeremiah 38 v 9)

Rescued

Jeremiah sat in the dark inside the well. There was no water in it. He sank down into thick, black mud.

He hadn't been there long when a servant at the palace went to see the king.

'Your Majesty,' the servant began, 'some men have thrown Jeremiah into a well. We can't just leave him there. It's not right.'

The king thought for a moment. Then –

'Find three men to go with you,' he ordered, 'and rescue Jeremiah.'

With ropes, the men pulled Jeremiah up out of the well.

God had kept His promise to look after him.

God made sure that Jeremiah was rescued.

Inside the well, do you think Jeremiah stopped trusting God – or do you think he asked Him for help?

Pens Prayer

Father God, I praise You that Your plans for me are perfect. Teach me to trust You always. Amen.

SUPER

'I tell you that he is the Son of God.'
(John 1 v 34)

No sleep

It was night. Tucked up in bed, Marco was wide awake.

Just down the road, so was Henry.

They were both too excited to sleep.

Marco and Henry had a hero. His name was SuperPen. They'd read about all his daring adventures in their favourite comic. And they'd just found out that he was going to star in his very own film!

'I'm never going to sleep again!' said Marco.

'If I manage to get to sleep,' said Henry, 'I'll eat my pillow!'

They just couldn't wait for the film to be shown in Pens' town cinema.

Being excited is heaps of fun! Let's get excited about knowing Jesus!

What do you get excited about?

Pens Prayer

Jesus, there is no one like You. Praise You! Amen.

35

Day 17 Super

'anyone who seeks will find'
(Matthew 7 v 8)

The 'big read'

In the middle of Marco's bedroom floor were some heaps of comics.

In the middle of the heaps sat Marco and Henry.

'What are you doing with all those comics?' asked Gloria. 'I'm sure you've read them before.'

'We have,' nodded Marco. 'But now we're having a "big read". We want to know SuperPen's adventures inside out and back to front before we go to see him in his film.'

'Oh, yes!' grinned Henry. 'Then we'll enjoy the film even more. And anyway, I'd be happy to read about SuperPen over and over and OVER again!'

Henry and Marco love reading about SuperPen. Let's get excited about reading stories of Jesus in the Bible.

What's your favourite story about Jesus?

Pens Prayer

Lord Jesus, the Bible teaches me so much about You. Help me to be excited about reading it. Amen.

'I love it when SuperPen rescues someone!' cried Marco.

'I love it when SuperPen swims faster than a motorboat!' squealed Henry.

'I love it when SuperPen climbs up the side of a building!' laughed Marco.

'I love it when SuperPen flies like an aeroplane!' beamed Henry.

'Are you *still* talking about SuperPen?' smiled Philippa. 'You've been chatting about him for ages.'

'That's because he's so brilliant!' said Marco and Henry.

'He must be,' replied Philippa. 'Do you know what I'm going to do? SuperPen's adventures sound so good, I'm going to start reading them myself.'

We can't stop talking when we're excited. Let's get excited when we talk about Jesus.

What amazing things has Jesus done?

Pens Prayer

Dear Jesus, You are amazing! Thank You for giving me so much to talk about. Amen.

39

Day 19 — Super

'Here we are, then, speaking for Christ' (2 Corinthians 5 v 20)

Poster Power!

'What we need to do,' said Marco, 'is to tell as many Pens as possible about SuperPen's film. We don't want them to miss it when it comes to Pens' town cinema.'

'How are we going to do that?' asked Henry.

Max had an idea.

'Why don't you make some posters?' he suggested.

So Marco and Henry made posters in bright colours. They included a picture of SuperPen and the words: 'SuperPen – The Movie – Coming to Pens' town cinema soon!'

Then Max helped Henry and Marco to put the posters up all around Pens' town.

 When we're excited, we want people to know why. Let's get excited and tell people that Jesus is our Friend.

own

What would you put on a poster about Jesus?

Pens Prayer

Lord Jesus, I want other people to know about You. Please help me to tell them. Amen.

41

Super

'Are any among you happy? They should sing praises.' (James 5 v 13)

The SuperPen song

Henry ran into Marco's garden.

'Listen, Marco!' he said. And he whistled a little tune.

42

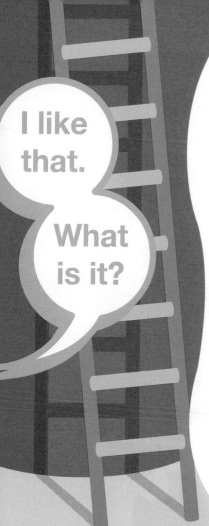

I like that.

What is it?

'Well,' said Henry, 'if we make up some words about SuperPen to go with it, we'll have our very own SuperPen song!'

The words to their SuperPen song went like this:

'SuperPen – he's a hero! SuperPen – he's the best! You'll know SuperPen when you see him – 'Cos SUPERPEN is written on his vest!'

Charlotte asked, 'May I sing your song, too, please?'

'Of course!' grinned Marco and Henry.

So Charlotte did. All across Pens' town.

 Henry is so excited about SuperPen that he wants to sing about him. Let's get excited and sing about Jesus.

Could you make up some special words to sing to Jesus?

Pens Prayer

Jesus, I want to sing praises to You! Thank You for loving to listen. Amen.

Day 21

Super

'How wonderful is the coming of messengers who bring good news!'
(Romans 10 v 15)

Fans

44

'*I know something you don't,*'
said Denzil to Marco and Henry.

'What's that?' Marco and Henry asked.

Denzil replied, 'SuperPen has a fan club.'

'*Really?*' Marco and Henry gasped!

'Lots of SuperPen fans belong
to it,' Denzil said. 'When you join,
you get a special comic just for club
members, and a big window sticker.'

'What's on the sticker?' squealed Henry.

'It says: "I'm a SuperPen fan!"' replied
Denzil. 'So anyone who sees it will
know how much you love SuperPen.'

'What are we waiting for, Henry?'
yelled Marco. 'We're joining the fan
club RIGHT NOW!'

Fans get excited about the
person they're a fan of. Let's be
fans of Jesus – and get excited!

What might a
sticker say to
show that you're
a fan of Jesus?

Pens Prayer

I love You, dear Jesus,
and I want everyone to
know! Amen.

45

Henry and Marco were playing at being SuperPen.

'I'm going to make sure everyone's happy!' yelled Marco.

'I'm going to see that no one's in trouble!' shouted Henry.

In their comics, Marco and Henry had read all about SuperPen. How he rescued and helped, brought happiness and sorted out trouble. He was a real superhero.

And Marco and Henry wanted to be just like him.

We want to be like our heroes. Let's get excited about trying to be like Jesus.

Would you like to be a superhero? How could you be super-kind to other people this week?

Pens Prayer

Lord Jesus, You are so loving and kind. Please teach me to be just like You. Amen.

47

Day 23 Super

'Jesus said to them, "Come with me"'
(Matthew 4 v 19)

Right now

48

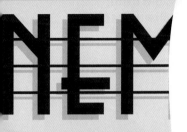

The time had come!

In Pens' town cinema, the SuperPen film had arrived.

'We don't need to go yet,' Squiggle said to Henry and Marco.

'No, we don't,' agreed Splodge. 'It doesn't start for ages.'

'But we want to go RIGHT NOW!' answered Marco. 'There'll be *lots* of Pens there. We want to make sure we get seats.'

'And not just any old seats,' added Henry. 'We want to be able to see EVERYTHING! We want the *best* seats in the whole cinema.'

So off they went, right then, to wait outside the cinema until the doors opened.

 Sometimes, we feel like we just can't wait for exciting things to happen! Let's get excited about spending time with Jesus.

You can talk to Jesus about anything and everything. What would you like to say to Him right now?

Pens Prayer

Thank You, Lord Jesus, that You love to hear from me. I want to be excited about spending time with You. Amen.

Day 24   Super

'Jesus answered ... "I am the way, the truth, and the life; no one goes to the Father except by me."' (John 14 v 6)

The **best** Superhero

Did you enjoy the film?

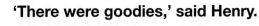

'There were goodies,' said Henry.

'And baddies,' grinned Marco.

'And SuperPen saved EVERYONE!' squeaked Henry.

'We're so excited,' laughed Marco, 'we're going to see it again tomorrow!'

Philippa smiled. 'Isn't being excited wonderful!' she said. 'And isn't Jesus exciting! He's God's very own Son. He came to earth to live with us, *just* so that He could teach us about God and show us how to be God's friends. Jesus really is a Superhero. The best Superhero in the whole wide world!'

 Because of Jesus, we can be with God forever. That's something to REALLY get excited about!

Yes!

The best Superhero deserves the best praise. What can you praise Jesus for right now?

Pens Prayer

Jesus, Son of God, I'm so excited that You want to be my Friend! Please help me always to be a good friend to You, too. Amen.

Day 25

'You are the Messiah, the Son of the living God.' (Matthew 16 v 16)

Son of God

Jesus had been working hard for His Father God.

He'd been teaching people about God's love for them.

He'd been meeting sick and disabled people and making them better.

He'd even walked on water!

Jesus' twelve special friends had spent lots of time with Him. They'd learnt more and more about Him. They'd seen miracle after miracle.

Now they were starting to understand that Jesus really was God's Son.

God sent His Son, Jesus, to live with us. He wanted Jesus to teach us how to be His friends.

Do you know what a 'miracle' is?

Pens Prayer

Thank You, dear Lord Jesus, for coming to live with us here on earth. Amen.

Once Upon a Mountain Top
Jesus shines!

Day 26

'Jesus … led them up a high mountain where they were alone.' (Matthew 17 v 1)

Time for friends

Jesus had something extra special He wanted to teach to three of His most faithful friends. So one day, He took them for a long walk.

Up, up, up they climbed.

Right to the top of a high mountain.

There was no one else on the mountain top when they got there, which was good. Jesus wanted them to be alone.

Sometimes Jesus spent time alone with His special friends, to teach them.

Do you ever play on your own? What do you like to do?

Pens Prayer

Thank You, Jesus, that I am never completely on my own. You are always with me. Amen.

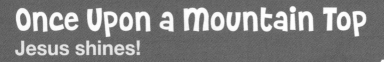

Once Upon a Mountain Top
Jesus shines!

Day 27

'a change came over Jesus: his face was shining like the sun' (Matthew 17 v 2)

Jesus' face

Peter, James and John were curious.

Why had Jesus brought them to a lonely mountain top?

What was it He wanted to say to them?

But Jesus didn't need to say anything at all.

As His three friends gazed at Him, suddenly His face began to glow with a brilliant light. It shone like the sun. And His clothes gleamed brighter than the brightest white!

Jesus' three friends stared. They couldn't take their eyes off Him. Never had they seen anything as amazing as this.

Jesus is the most amazing Man who has ever lived.

Who do you think covered Jesus in light?

Pens Prayer

Jesus, You are God's very own Son, but You still want to be my Friend. Praise You! Amen.

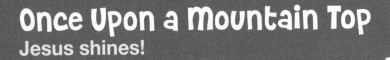

Once Upon a Mountain Top
Jesus shines!

Day 28

'This is my own dear Son, with whom I am pleased' (Matthew 17 v 5)

The voice

Peter, James and John gazed in wonder at Jesus.

All of a sudden, there was even more brightness!

A shining cloud appeared. It drifted towards them. And as it moved closer, they heard a voice from the cloud speaking to them.

'This is my very own Son,' the voice said. 'I love Him and I am so pleased with Him. You must listen to Him.'

 God wanted Jesus' friends to know exactly who Jesus was.

At sunrise and sunset, the sky and the clouds sometimes glow. What colours do they glow with?

Pens Prayer

Father God, thank You so much for sending Your Son to teach us all about You. Amen.

Once Upon a Mountain Top
Jesus shines!

Day 29

'"Get up," [Jesus] said. "Don't be afraid!"'
(Matthew 17 v 7)

Hiding

When Peter, James and John heard the voice speak out of the cloud, they were terrified!

Their eyes grew huge. Their knees trembled.

They couldn't look at the cloud any longer. They threw themselves down on the ground and hid their faces.

Jesus walked towards them. He reached out a hand and touched them.

'It's all right, my friends,' He said. 'There's no need to be frightened. Come on – up you get.'

Jesus wasn't afraid. He knew His Father's voice.

Think of the people you know really well. If you couldn't see them, would you know their voices?

Pens Prayer

Jesus, Son of God, with You beside me, I never need to be afraid. Thank You. Amen.

Once Upon a Mountain Top
Jesus shines!

Day 30 'they looked up and saw no one there but Jesus.' (Matthew 17 v 8)

One day

Very slowly, Jesus' friends lifted their heads.

First they looked at Jesus.

Then they glanced all around.

The cloud had gone. They were alone again with Jesus on the mountain top.

Peter, James and John scrambled to their feet.

'Listen to me,' said Jesus. 'You mustn't tell anyone what you have seen here. Not yet. But the time will come,' He added, 'when I want you to tell everyone all about me.'

When Jesus had finished speaking, He led His three friends back down the mountain.

One day, Jesus' friends would be so excited to know Him that they wouldn't be able to keep quiet about Him.

If you want to tell someone about Jesus, who will give you the right words to say?

Pens Prayer

Lord Jesus, I'm so excited to know You! You're my best Friend and I want to be Yours! Amen.